Pacific Passage

Contents

Written by Shilo Berry

Illustrated by Elena Petrov

February 20

Hello, and welcome to our web page.

We hope you will check in with us as we sail across the Pacific Ocean on a journey that will take us to the country where our grandfather was born, and which will be full of fun and learning.

We will leave from Cabo San Lucas, Baja, California, and arrive in Auckland, New Zealand a year later, having stopped at many places along the way.

Let us introduce the people who will be on board. There are Charlie and Samantha (that's us); our parents, Jacy and Ben; and our grandparents, Pita (Peter) and Nell.

Our grandfather, Pita, first came to Seattle while he was working as a crew member on a yacht. He only intended staying for a short time on a work visa but he met and eventually married our grandmother, Nell.

Luckily Nell shared Pita's passion for sailing and everything having to do with it. When Ben was born, Nell and Pita introduced him to boats and boating as soon as they could.

When Ben met our mother, Jacy, he managed to convince her that sailing was the best thing since sliced bread. So it was no surprise that we were brought up to have the same appreciation and passion for sailing as the rest of the family. We were aboard a ship before we were even born!

The idea of sailing all the way to New Zealand came up when Grandpa came to tell us about a family reunion. We were all excited, not only because we had heard so much about the country

he had been born in, but because we desperately wanted to meet our distant relatives. We couldn't help wondering if they'd be into sailing, too!

When our parents suggested we take a year off work and school and sail across the Pacific, it was like all our wishes had come true. Imagine a year without school! What a dream.

Unfortunately, that is not quite what is happening. We have to do correspondence school and this web page is our year-long project.

So here we go. We hope you can check in on a regular basis and follow our progress through these Internet reports. If you would like to get in touch with us, you could send us an e-mail at charlieandsamantha@acrossthepacific.com.

Charlie and Samantha

March 3

Well, here we are in Cabo San Lucas. You are probably wondering how we got here.

The truth is, Dad and Grandpa sailed the boat down from Seattle. They thought the trip to Nuku Hiva in the Marquesas would be better started

from here than from Seattle. So the rest of us flew here while Dad and Grandpa sailed down.

We have been here for about a week now, getting the last-minute things ready for the trip. There has been such a lot to organize! It'll be good to get underway at last.

The seawater is warm and we have managed to make plenty of time for swimming. It really is amazing. We've been lucky enough to see humpback whales, lots of bottlenose dolphins, and manta rays. They don't seem to be scared of the boat at all and sometimes come very close. The dolphins jump in and out of the water. We watch them for hours. It's hard to get motivated to do our schoolwork when there is so much else to do!

We have spent a lot of time on the shore and have met some locals. They seem friendly and are very helpful, but communication is difficult because of the language differences. Dad speaks a

smattering of Spanish, but the rest of us don't know any.

We set sail tomorrow on a trip that could take us anywhere between 15 and 20 days.

We will be in touch throughout the journey, so keep checking in for updates.

Charlie and Samantha

March 10

I still don't have my sea legs. I've never been seasick before, so I don't know why it's happening now! Charlie says it's because we're out on the open ocean, and the northeast trade winds have been blowing which makes the boat roll around a

lot. He is perfectly fine and so is everyone else. He teases me all the time about being sick. I wish he'd leave me alone!

Because of the high winds and rough seas, our parents and Grandpa have been taking turns staying up during the night on lookout. They wear a harness while up on deck. Charlie and I are not allowed on deck while the wind and swells are like this because the adults say it is too dangerous.

Dad says the sea is much rougher than anyone could have predicted. But last night was the worst. We awoke to hear a loud crashing on the deck. Our parents and Grandpa were up on deck.

We could hear our mother's voice yelling to get the sails down to try and slow the boat down. We were moving quickly and that gave us less control in the wild weather.

Grandma wouldn't let us go up on the deck so we were forced to stay down below. She had a look on her face that we knew not to challenge.

"Get your wet-weather and safety gear on quickly," she said, pulling on her own life jacket.

I felt really sick because the boat was rolling around so much. We were stuck below with no fresh air, and I didn't know what was happening on deck. It was very frightening.

We heard our mother shout again, trying to get Dad and Grandpa to hurry. She had panic in her voice. She was having a lot of trouble holding the wheel, but the two men couldn't help because they urgently needed to get the sails down.

There was another loud crash and we heard the sound of water pouring over the deck, then a loud snapping and thumping noise.

Our mother was screaming and yelling. Dad and Grandpa were yelling. Grandma's face was deathly pale as she tried to calm us down.

"It's the mast," Charlie was yelling at her. "We have to go up and help!"

But Grandma stood firm. There was no way we were going to get past her. I hadn't realized she was quite so strong.

The boat was rolling to one side. Our mother was shouting to the others, "Cut it away! It's pulling us over!"

Grandpa and Dad would have been working as fast as they could, but it didn't seem fast enough, especially to the three of us down below where we couldn't see what was going on. We could only feel the swaying, rocking motion and hear wind and sea and shouting.

"We're going over! We're going over!" I kept saying. I knew it didn't help but I couldn't stop.

Charlie was still trying to get past Grandma. She was still holding firm. "If you go up there, Charlie, you'll get swept over the side," she was saying. "We'd never be able to pick you up in this weather and in the dark."

Suddenly, the boat rolled back upright. The dreadful noise of the waves smashing against the boat was much quieter now. The boat was rolling less and didn't seem to be moving so quickly. I breathed a sigh of relief.

The three of us were huddled on the stairs

listening to the sound of voices above. Although we were not yet out of danger, the voices of our parents and Grandpa seemed less panicked.

Grandpa called down to us to say that everything would be okay, but to stay down below until the storm subsided. Great.

It was another two hours or so before our mother finally came down with a look of relief on her tired face. She was weighed down with heavy wet-weather gear and other safety gear – her life jacket and harness. One look at her, pale and soaked to the skin, told us that she was absolutely exhausted. The others would be, too. It had been a rough time and they'd all worked hard for hours without a break.

Our grandmother radioed to let the rescue patrol know our position, and tell them that we had lost our mast, but that we would be able to rig something up to enable us to get to Nuku Hiva,

although it would be very slowly.

Things are a little better now. The weather's slightly improved, I'm not feeling so sick, and we're all okay.

We'll keep you posted.

Samantha

March 16

After our stormy night, things got better – well, they couldn't have got too much worse. Our boat limped slowly along for the next couple of days. With the rigged mast and much smaller sail we were not going anywhere fast. The wind dropped

right down, too, making us extra slow. The trip will probably take us about five extra days now. We don't mind, though, as we're happy just to be out of danger.

We are short on some food rations but at least there are plenty of fish in the sea, and our water distiller is working overtime.

We spend the days catching as many fish as we can. Grandma is especially good at it. She got three yesterday within minutes of each other. They're mostly big bonitos. Bonitos are a type of tuna fish with dark stripes on them. We eat them for most meals! Apart from fishing, Charlie and I have been doing schoolwork and helping the others out around the boat.

Talk to you again soon.

Samantha

March 17

Hi again. I just had to write another quick update because this morning we saw something really worth writing about.

As usual, we were all up early – just as the sun was coming up. We go to bed when it's getting dark

and get up when it starts to get light. Anyway, Charlie and I went up on deck to get some fresh air and watch the spectacular sunrise when I suddenly saw a big dark shape in the water, not too far from the boat. I yelled out to Charlie, thinking it might be a shark, but then, just as Charlie came over to peer over the side, we saw the shape leap up out of the water and splash back in. It was enormous! It was a huge whale. It stayed near the boat for quite a while, playing and checking us out.

We called the others up on deck and we had breakfast watching the whale's antics. Dad told us that when whales pop their heads out of the water and stay balanced that way, up on their tail, it's called spy hopping.

I think seeing the whale made us all feel better about losing the mast.

Samantha

March 21

Samantha spoke too soon! It seemed like we had just got over the high winds and rough seas and settled into some fishing and maintenance on the boat when we encountered more trouble. It was the last thing we were expecting.

The weather was fairly calm so only one person was staying up on watch at a time. It must have been about midnight because Dad and Grandpa were just about to change watch when it happened. There was an almighty bang, the boat listed sideways, and then sort of stopped dead in its tracks.

We were all awake in a flash, stunned. Then everyone leapt into action. Our mother was throwing safety gear in our direction and telling us to stay put with our grandmother while she found out what was going on up top. It sounded like a repeat of the last time – Samantha and I stuck below deck with Grandma standing guard.

The sounds from above told us that Dad and Grandpa were running to the front of the boat. There was a lot of shouting and we realized that our suspicions that we might have hit something were probably correct.

Our mother was passing lanterns and harnesses up to Dad and Grandpa. Luckily the sea was relatively calm because we needed to assess the damage and that meant someone had to go over the side. It sounded like it was going to be Dad.

Our mother then came back down and went to the front of the boat to see if any water was forcing its way into the boat. When she returned, we could tell immediately by the look on her face that things could have been better. She was frowning and chewing her lip. She didn't say anything but gave us a quick smile as she went to pass on whatever the news was to Dad and Grandpa.

Samantha and I looked at each other. We were both scared because we didn't really know what was going on or what might happen. Things were made worse by the fact that we were never allowed to help in these dangerous situations and we really wanted to.

Once again, Grandma was keeping calm. As usual, her job was to look after us and keep us out of the way. She was excellent at it, too. As we've learned, getting past Grandma when she doesn't want you to is pretty much impossible.

Dad and Grandpa came down and worked with our mother to help set up the bilge pump. That could only mean one thing – the boat was taking on water. I could tell Samantha was starting to panic, so I pointed out that the adults didn't look too worried so she shouldn't be, either. And it was true. Surprisingly, the look on their faces was not one of panic, but almost of relief. We still had no idea what was really going on, though, and that was what made the situation so frightening.

After some time, we all met in the galley to assess our situation and discuss the plan of attack. Dad told us that we had hit a partially floating container. Apparently they are not uncommon in

these waters. They just fall off cargo ships and are left bobbing around in the open water like junk. They are very dangerous for boats the size of ours as there is no way of avoiding them, especially at night! They are quite large.

Grandpa told us that part of the hull was cracked, but at this stage it was above the waterline and, although the odd wave was leaking in, our bilge pump would be able to pump the seawater out – unless we struck rough seas again, of course.

So Samantha and I finally figured out that that was why they were relieved – it could have been worse. No one said anything, but we all knew that if the crack in the hull had been bigger and if no one had been able to get to us in time, we could all easily have drowned in the open seas.

Grandma radioed on to Nuku Hiva telling them our position, current situation, and expected time

of arrival. At this time, if the weather held, we would not need a support vessel.

Nuku Hiva is a French-speaking port so Grandma was our translator. They answered that they would keep a lookout for us, that the weather was looking good for the next week, and to keep in touch each day so that they could be sure we were okay.

That was really all that we could do. Knowing that we were only a couple of days away, even at our slow pace, was a huge relief.

That's it for now.

Charlie

March 24

We finally rounded the point and limped into the safety of the waters just off Nuku Hiva. We were all extremely glad to have arrived.

Now we have to wait for the *Aranui*, a supply ship that comes in about every three weeks from Tahiti,

to get the parts we need for the repairs to our boat's mast and the hull. In the meantime, we're going to relax and try to enjoy ourselves while we're here. It's nice to be on dry land for a change. And Nuku Hiva will be a beautiful place to explore. I can't wait.

It is a very green, steep island with many waterfalls. In fact, the largest waterfall in the South Pacific is on this island. It's called Ahuii. We'll be going to see it in the next couple of days. You need to take guides as it is quite a long way upriver and you have to do some walking through areas of jungle. It can be dangerous and difficult for people who are unfamiliar with the terrain. That's us! Dad's going to organize it.

The water is incredibly clear and we've been swimming a lot. The fish are very bright and fascinating to look at, but there are also many sharks, so we keep close to the shore! The local

people say the sharks are scared of us and it does seem that way because they never come close. I'm glad. I do not like the idea of coming face to face with a shark, no matter how scared it might be.

It's good to see that the smile has returned to my grandma's face. It tells me that she is hugely relieved that the difficulties of the past few weeks are behind us and that she is feeling relaxed.

The adults have been in deep discussion about whether to continue the trip because of the difficulties we've encountered so far. Dad says we should hold a meeting and take a vote, each of us keeping in mind what is best for the family as a whole. We're going to give ourselves some time to think about it, then hold the meeting, but I know I want to continue and Charlie feels the same way. We've come this far. It'd be really sad to stop now. And what would we do with the boat, anyway?

We'll probably wait until we've been to see Ahuii

before we post another page about our adventures, so check back in a few days for more.

Samantha

March 28

We couldn't go up to the waterfall until yesterday because heavy rain had swollen the river, making it muddy and dangerous. We had to wait for it to settle back down.

We had a great time meeting friendly locals

and swimming while we were waiting, though. The water is warm and there are plenty of fish to look at and catch.

We set off through the jungle for our starting point up the river yesterday morning. We had to carry our two small boats. They were like a cross between a dinghy and a canoe. My grandmother, father, and I were going to be in one boat with two local guides. My grandfather, Samantha, and my mother were going to be in the other one with two more guides.

After a taxing walk up through the jungle beside the river, the guides told us to put down the boats. Our journey down the river was about to begin!

The water in the river is very different from the water in the sea. For a start it is fresh, not salt. It has different hues of blue and green as well. Although it was still a bit churned up from the rain, it was a light bluish green. It didn't seem very deep

in most places and we could see rocks on the bottom and sometimes even fish.

As we moved downstream the water seemed to be moving fairly rapidly. The two guides didn't have to paddle much, except to keep us near the middle of the river.

Then, after we had journeyed downstream for some time, the guides told us the height of the waterfall. It sure is high! They said that in another five minutes or so we would have to take a fork in the river that would take us through some gentle rapids and bring us out below the waterfall.

Along the sides of the river, we could see that parts of the bank had fallen into the river. The guides explained that it was due to the heavy downpours over the last couple of days.

The river was moving faster now and the guides were having to paddle more to keep us on track. They were speaking in French and by the look on

Grandma's face, I could tell something was wrong.

The boats moved faster and faster. Now the guides in each boat were shouting across to each other. My heart began to beat faster and faster. I was glad of the life jackets we were all wearing.

Grandma was urgently translating what the guides were saying and passing it on to us. Dad was trying to help paddle to get us to the side of the river. It was hard work. Dad's face was straining every time he dug his paddle into the water.

Grandma held on tightly to me as we sat in the bottom of the boat. I had lost track of the other boat, but felt slightly relieved when Grandma said they had managed to steer our boat down the fork that led to the bottom of the waterfall. Little did I know that ahead of us lay the gentle rapids, which were no longer gentle, but had turned into rushing, roaring rapids with large rocks sticking out of the water everywhere.

There was nothing we could do. We hit the first rock and were thrown into the air, landing heavily in the raging river. There wasn't even time to scream. Every time I opened my mouth, water flooded into it. I spluttered and tried to catch my breath each time my head came to the surface.

The force of the water kept pushing me back under again. I tried to convince myself not to panic, but I was! I don't know how many times I bobbed up and down under the water. I do know that I was really tired when I was thrown hard against something, which turned out to be two large boulders. There was nowhere to hold on to, but at least the width of the boulders stopped me from rolling downstream. Finally, I managed to keep my head up and get a big breath even though the water was pounding hard against my chest.

Within seconds of stopping, something else hit me and then grabbed hold. It was Grandma. She was out of breath. We stayed there, hardly able to move or say anything, but the look on Grandma's face said it all. I think my face probably had the same look. We were both alive. Now we just needed to get out of there.

We managed to turn ourselves around so the

pounding water was on our backs and then Grandma started singing! At first I thought she was being silly but then I realized she was trying to keep herself awake, so I joined in. I'm not sure how many songs we sang, but we kept going until we heard voices calling from the riverbank. Looking across I could see that although the riverbank was close, there was a wild rushing flood of water between us and it.

I hadn't realized that Grandma had stopped singing until the people on the riverbank tried to throw us a rope. It was then that I realized she was actually unconscious! She had placed her body between me and the full force of the pounding river to protect me from it.

Now it was my turn to help her. I somehow needed to keep her head out of the water while they pulled us across to the side of the river. My hands were numb, but I managed to tie the rope

around us both and then kick off from the boulders, at the same time getting behind my grandmother. With much bobbing underwater, we were gradually pulled to the side.

The first person I saw was Dad. He had managed to make it to the side with one of the guides, who had then run off to get help. The other guide was still missing. Others were looking for him.

My grandmother was crouched spluttering beside me. Thank goodness she was conscious again. I'd been so worried about her.

We were both loaded onto stretchers ready to be carried back to the town for medical attention.

As soon as he knew Grandma and I were safe, Dad rushed off into the jungle with some of the helpers. It wasn't until we got back to the town that we learned that the others hadn't been found yet. It was then that the terror really set in. We wanted to go back and help, but neither of us had the strength

to move. I wanted to cry, but I didn't even have the strength to do that, so we just held each other, hoping we would see the rest of our family alive.

Charlie

That was Charlie's version of events. This is mine.

When we first started the boat ride to the waterfall, I was thinking how wonderfully peaceful the river and its surroundings were. But in a very short time my thoughts had changed drastically.

First, the river began moving faster and faster, then the guides began talking louder and louder. Even though we couldn't understand what they were saying, their tone said all was not well.

Grandpa pushed me down into the bottom of the boat and he and my mother helped the guides to paddle. They were pointing to the sides of the river but the banks were steep so we wouldn't have been able to get out anyway. It wasn't until we went one way and the other boat went another way that I realized there was a major problem. Either we were heading for the top of the waterfall or the other boat was. The look on our guides' faces told the story. We were in serious trouble.

Our boat rushed frantically through rapidly moving water. Rocks and boulders began showing in the water and the water was thrashing against them. We managed to steer our way through much of the rapids, getting thrown from side to side with water pouring into the boat. I think I spent a lot of the time screaming. My mother and grandfather were trying to keep the boat upright, but also keep us away from the rocks.

Somehow through all the noise, hard work, and language barriers the guides managed to let my grandfather know that our only chance was a small pool just before the top of the waterfall. If we made it that far, we would have to jump to the left side of the boat and hope to be caught by a lip of rock that would channel us into shallow water. Our timing had to be perfect, otherwise we would be thrown over the waterfall and drowned.

There was no time to really digest the

information or even think at all. The guides were signaling to Grandpa, pointing to the area up ahead. We could see it as the boat was bounced up and down in the rushing water. The guides pushed us to the left side of the boat. Grandpa grabbed one of my hands and my mother the other. At the last minute, the guides threw their paddles over the side and we all jumped in together.

Swishing and swirling in the water we were sucked under and up again. Each time I came up I tried to catch my breath. Then my hands slipped away from the others'. All I could think about was that I was going over the falls when, suddenly, I hit something with a thud and my body was thrown in another direction. I began sliding down, down, down, and then I splashed awkwardly into a small still pool.

Someone grabbed me and dragged me to the side of the pool and I realized that we'd made it.

We hadn't gone over the waterfall but had hit the lip, which had been the plan. The slide was the natural rock and water concourse that had brought us into the pool. I lay by the side of the river tired and weak. The two guides were there and my mother and grandfather. I looked around and started to cry. It was hard to believe what we'd just been through, and even harder to believe that we had all survived.

I knew the others were thinking the same thing. My mother was silent, but she held me tightly. Grandpa took charge again after a minute or so. He wanted to get back to see if the others were all right. He was very worried, but trying hard not to let it show. There was still work to do.

After a rest, we began our slow journey back through the jungle, the guides leading the way. After about ten minutes we thought we heard someone calling. Then we saw Dad come running through the jungle.

It was an emotional reunion and we were overjoyed to hear that the others were back in town, receiving medical attention. We would soon be there ourselves. Whew. I have to stop now but I'll write more soon.

Samantha

April 10

Grandma is still recovering in the hospital. She really took a battering while she was protecting Charlie from the pounding water. She managed to break several ribs. The staff at the hospital say she will make a complete recovery, but it will be some

time before she is back to her old self again. We visit her every day. Grandpa spends most of his time at the hospital, keeping her entertained.

We will stay on here until she is ready to travel again. Apart from emotional damage, the rest of us came out of the incident relatively unhurt, thank goodness. It could have been so much worse.

There is some bad news, though. One of the guides has not been found yet. He is presumed drowned. There was a memorial service held for him this morning beside the river. We all attended, except Grandma. It was very emotional. All his family were there and the tears flowed.

The people in the town have been very kind to us, offering us places to stay and gifts of food. We were extremely grateful to them but we felt we needed to stay on the boat.

We finally held our meeting, having had plenty of time to think about things. We had it at the hospital

in Grandma's room. We'd thought that if there was one person who would vote not to continue, it would have to be Grandma, but we should have known better. The first thing she said was, "When do we set sail?" Our parents just looked at each other and smiled. Grandpa was beaming, too.

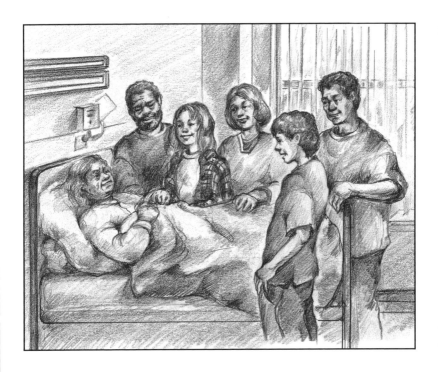

So, it looks like we're going to continue, but not yet. We've decided to stay here for a few more months. We're going to do everything we possibly can to get the boat in top shape before we leave. And we're going to wait for Grandma to be in top shape, too.

Our experiences have not turned us off water or boating at all, but rather made us more determined to carry on. They've also made us realize that if we hadn't been so well prepared or didn't have the knowledge and boating sense that we have, things could have been a lot worse. Most of all we are glad that even though we have been through a lot, we are all still together as a family and we'll carry on that way.

Charlie and Samantha